FOREWORD BY JANE HERBERT
(Johnny's mummy)

I would like to thank Jim for asking me to write the foreword for his new book.

We have had a great year, and Johnny's wins at Silverstone and Monza gave us all a little something to celebrate. It was fabulous after all the years of hard work, but through it all Johnny never gave up, and he never lost his sense of humour.

The Pits is a witty and humourous look at motor racing. The detail he puts into the cartoon is brilliant, especially with the short time he has to come up with the caption and punchline. There is always something a little special to look for. And I know that Johnny enjoys them as well as the rest of our family.

We would like to wish Jim every success for many years to come.

Jane Herbert

Jane Herbert, Margaretting Tye, Essex

A JEREMY CLARKSON FREE ZONE

ACKNOWLEDGEMENTS/APOLOGIES
(please delete which applicable)
Autosport magazine, with special thanks
to Keith Oswin, who thinks he thinks of my ideas,
and to the editor Bruce 'red pen' Jones, who actually does!
Cars and Car Conversions, Autocar, Racecar Engineering.
Volvo, TWR, Rothmans, Williams, Ann Bradshaw, Taki Inoue,
Mike and Sue Greasley, David Richards, Quentin Spurring,
Will Hoy, Penske Cars, McLaren, Steve Matchett,
Barrie Hinchliffe, John Cleland, Derek Warwick,
and the nurses of room 135.

Produced by Autosport Special Projects
Reproduced by Primary Colours, Chiswick, London
Printed by BR Hubbard Ltd, Sheffield

for Mike and Sue

Captain Marvel, laughing all the way to the bank.

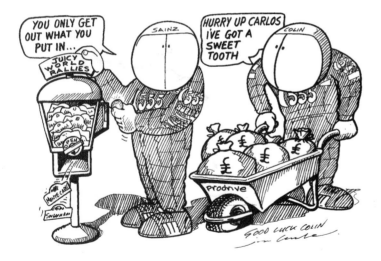

Sorry Possum!

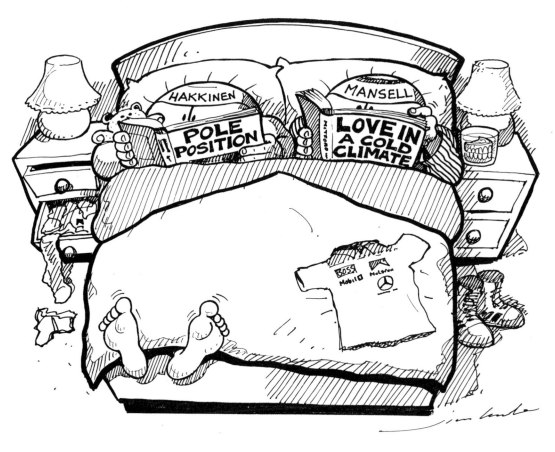

Come on, be honest, you never expected it to work, did you?

11

12

Alas poor Warwick, he was to suffer throughout the year the slings and arrows of outrageous fortune!

13

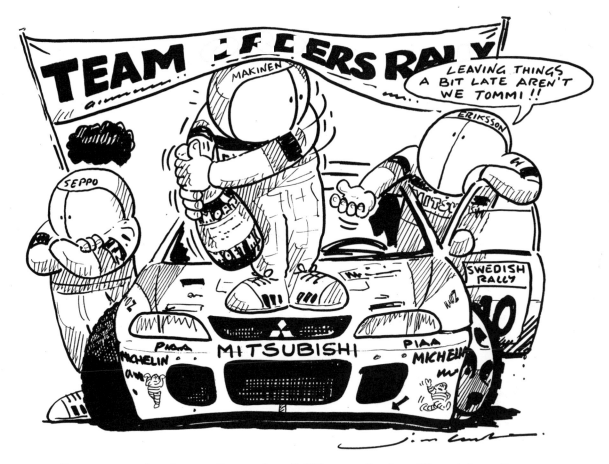

Do you remember the wrestling on the telly? That was fixed too. Where is it now?

15

It's Batman and Robin!

17

It was cold at Silverstone in March, damn cold!

In pre-season testing at Estoril, it was fast Eddie who was quicker

Over the pond the best Indycar team of 1994 Penske, were nowhere!

23

Mansell decided to sit out the first GP of the season and one of the Brundell brothers was asked to drive in his place. The reason?............I think was because Mark had smaller elbows than Mansell,but please correct me if I'm wrong.

25

.........some lawyer somewhere!

The young two year old Volvo out of TWR was doing the early running.

29

QUACK, QUACK

Looking at this afresh I think 'BONK' isn't quite right.

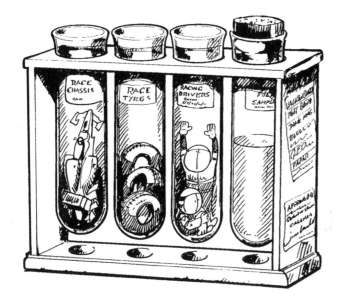

32

No such luck! Damon got a Ducati Monster 900 and Georgie......a fitted kitchen!

PODIUMS-R-US

To everyone's surprise, Volvo and TWR just kept on winning.

Life in the fast lane!

37

38

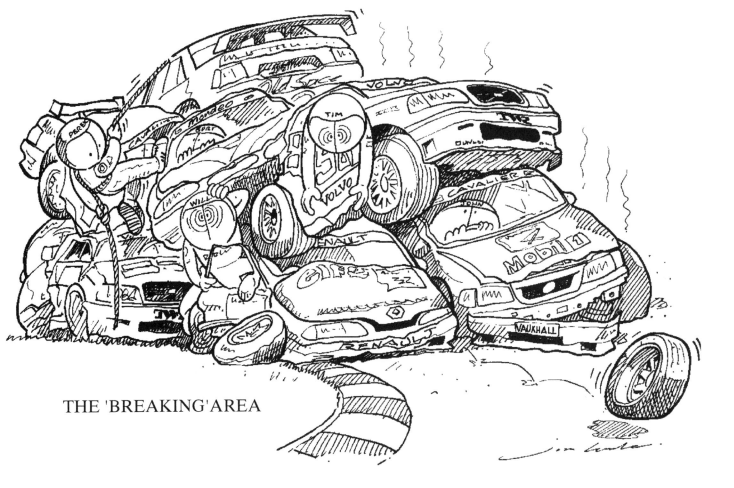

THE 'BREAKING' AREA

A lot of the BTCC races were shrouded in a strange red mist.

M for **M**cLaren, **M**ercedes, **M**obil, **M**ika, **M**ansell and **M**ediocrity.
May was a bad month for the Penske/McLaren combo.

41

42

Mansell had left McLaren,surprise,surprise and Penske had failed to qualify for the Indy 500,shock,horror!!

When Captain Marvel finally left the unhappy marriage with McLaren
it was up to the indefatigable Mark Blunder to fill the enlarged breech.

This was for the mad doctors at Castle Combe

48

CANADIAN WAR-DANCE

If you don't know the song, this isn't funny, so ask a friend to sing it for you!

49

Our very own Del boy, trying to salvage something from the year.

52

Will Hoy likes to remind me that this was his buckin' idea.

— McLAREN'S "BAGUETTE"

The original caption for this was about the McLarens main sponsor, a vasectomy clinic, but it was cut.

It never happened-the same old bore's still there!

58

Michael Schumacher-F1's one man band. Nice song, shame about the video!

59

Looking back to the British GP,it's clear that Damon, just for a second, thought he was Alesi!

"McLAREN'S NEW DRIVER IS RUNNING RINGS ROUND THE OPPOSITION!"

...........dream on Ron.
Juan Manuel Fangio, the greatest racing driver of all time, died this year. He was 84

If Johnny was pleased about his win, the nurses of room 135,
Plymouth General Hospital must have been ecstatic!

65

..........no it isn't Patrick Head dressed up!

After Damon went out there was no competition and Schumacher walked it!

70

For Will Hoy,the association with Williams was a distinct advantage! in August he won his first race
for the Williams Renault team.

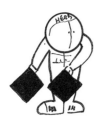

As you can imagine Taki wasn't too pleased at this!

Hill and Schumacher, at one point they were the Vinnie Jones and Gazza of F1.

Ginger Bamber?

In your anniversary supplement, I was struck by the resemblance between Jim Bamber and celebrated drummer Ginger Baker. I wonder if they could perhaps be related. I think we should be told – and I think Taki Inoue should certainly be told!

Mike Naylor
High Wycombe, Buckinghamshire

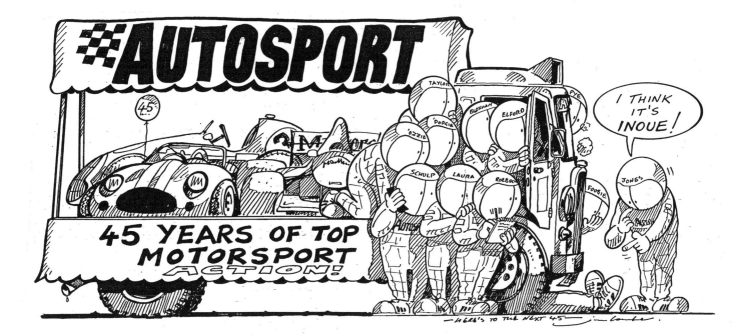

Yes I did meet Inoue at the Autosport party and no I don't look like Ginger Baker!

Here's to the next 45!

After the British Grand Prix, both drivers were warned about their
future conduct and naturally for the rest of the year were as good as gold.......
...........well, except at Spa....and Monza........................and the Nurburgring!

At Spa, Michael Schumacher started the race in Holland, and still won!

83

After Berger decided to follow Alesi to Benetton, Herbert's days at the team were numbered.

Herbert might have missed the bus for '96, but he still managed to walk off with his second Grand Prix win of the year.

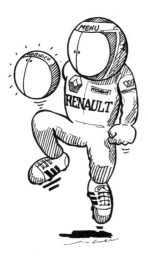

WHEEL TO WHEEL COMBAT!

The Renault boys, Menu and Hoy, won both races at the BTCC Silverstone finale
and snatched the makes title from Vauxhall.

89

_ 'IT'S A GOOD FUN CIRCUIT'
RICHARD RYDELL

Remember, Michael, Irvine is right behind you!

In September, one of my favourite drivers, got married. Mark Blundell on the front row at last!

A disastrous weekend for McLaren at Estoril with their pick 'n' mix chassis selection
reduced to a lottery.

95

I think you'll find the answer is written on an Adelaide wall!

The BTCBS or to you and me-the British Touring Car Boot Sale!

99

From the ring- side it did seem that Williams were not giving Hill their full support.

I bet it's Margaret who has to polish it all!

Ralph Firman at Silverstone demonstrating the F3 equivalent of an own goal!

SEEN IN JAPAN

Young Magnussen, standing in for Mika, must have been chuffed with his performance in far flung Aida.........

107

...........very, very chuffed!

'Many a slip between cup and lip'

The Williams pair, preparing their defences against the forthcoming verbal assault from Patrick Head and the massed ranks of the media.

Spotted on the A23 just outside Croydon, picking the flies from his teeth!

The FIA acted swiftly when Toyota was caught cheating on the Catalunya Rally in November.

"Is there a Fairy God-Mother in the house?"

119

Thanks Damon, great idea!

Colin McRae and the RAC Rally upstaged by our very own Princess Di.

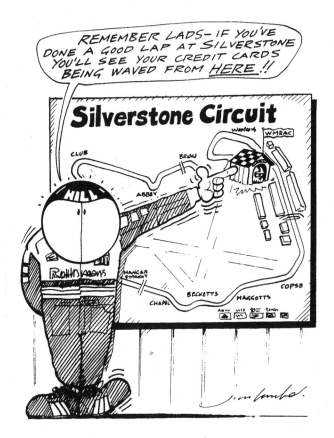

The infamous ladies of the WMRAC strutting their stuff at the Doghouse Ball.